Risk Assessment

A Line Manager's Guide

Pat McGuinness

THE INDUSTRIAL SOCIETY

First published in 1995 by
The Industrial Society
Robert Hyde House
48 Bryanston Square
London W1H 7LN
Telephone: 0171-262-2401

© *The Industrial Society 1995*

ISBN 1 85835 164 2

British Library Cataloguing-in-Publication Data.
A Catalogue record for this book is available from the
British Library.

Typeset by: Cheryl Zimmerman
Printed by: Bourne Press
Cover Design: Chambers Chapman

The Industrial Society is a Registered
Charity No. 290003

Contents

Foreword...vii

Introduction 1

1 Background..5

2 Recent Legislation requiring Risk Assessment..........9

3 Recent Legislation requiring Risk Assessment
   (Northern Ireland)...25

4 Methods of Carrying Out Risk Assessments 31

5 How to Set Up a Risk Assessment Programme.......43

6 Assessing Effectiveness.....................................47

7 References..49

8 Appendices 53

   1 Useful Addresses 54

   2 Assessment Checklist Proforma.......................55

   3 HSE Risk Assessment Form.............................60

   4 How The Industrial Society can Help.................64

   5 Non-exhaustive list of Agents, Processes and
      Working Conditions..65

Foreword

Every organisation must carry out health and safety risk assessments; there is no choice, it is a clear legal requirement.

It is most likely that those assigned to this role will be covered by the broad title of line managers. This book is designed to explain to those managers, supervisors, team leaders, section heads, etc why health and safety risk assessments are necessary, and how to go about implementing them. It provides an overview of the legal requirements, and some ideas on how to address them, together with details of various practical approaches to risk assessment.

We would point out that the background notes on legislation should not be regarded as legal interpretation, or legal documents in themselves. The purpose of including these notes is to raise awareness and set the risk assessment process in context.

You are strongly advised to obtain copies of the HSE or HSA documents referred to in the text, details of which appear in the References at the end of the book.

Probably the most important factor in determining the success of your risk assessment programme will be how far you enlist the help of those people who actually carry out the tasks of your organisation. Take every possible opportunity to involve as many of them as possible in the risk assessment programme.

Pat McGuinness

Introduction

Every year about 500 people die in work-related accidents; 30 million working days are lost through injury or ill health. And studies have shown that about 1.6 million accidents occur in the workplace each year in the UK.

The appalling human cost of this is difficult to comprehend unless you are unfortunate enough to have been involved as either victim, relative, colleague or manager. The financial implications both for organisations and the country's economy are staggering.

Health and Safety Executive (HSE) studies indicate that the overall cost of work accidents to employers is estimated at between £4 billion and £9 billion per year. This is equal to between 5% and 10% of gross trading profits. And the same studies put the true cost to the UK economy of work accidents and work-related ill health at between £10 billion and £15 billion a year, or 1.75%–2.75% of the country's gross domestic product.

With this background it is easy to understand why new and more specific legislation is being introduced.

The new legislation makes explicit what was implicit in the Health and Safety at Work Act 1974, focusing on what needs to be done to raise the standard of our management of health and safety at work.

It is also of interest, but in view of the above not surprising, to note the consistent rise in fines for breaches of health and safety legislation. Organisations which break the law can expect to receive large fines, together with extensive legal costs. Individuals who are proven to have breached the law are often prosecuted, and include directors, managers, supervisors and employees. Penalties range from personal fines, community service awards to, in severe cases involving indictment to crown court, unlimited fines and/or imprisonment!

The current maximum fine on summary conviction (in a magistrates court) for breaches of sections 2–6 of the Health and Safety at Work Act 1974 is £20,000 per breach. For other areas of health and safety legislation the current maximum fine on summary conviction is £5,000. And there can be many breaches in a single accident. Clearly the management of health and safety at work (or lack of it) represents a serious problem.

Unfortunately employers often regard this area as a 'bolt on' activity and do little if anything to pursue it with the same rigour that they apply to other activities, unless they are unfortunate and suffer a serious accident. Then the situation changes dramatically, as senior management become involved and time, money and effort are expended in reactive measures.

In contrast, **risk assessment** offers a proactive approach, helping organisations to avoid incurring losses by preventing the accidents happening in the first place. Properly implemented, an effective risk assessment programme will make the organisation more efficient at what it does.

1 Background

The requirement to carry out risk assessments is driven by the three main reasons for managing health and safety at work.

1 Moral reasons

No organisation would wish to see people injured or killed in the workplace. It is extremely upsetting for all concerned when a serious accident takes place. It is difficult to have to tell the relatives of the injured what has happen to their loved one. And it is even more difficult to attend the funeral of someone who has died carrying out his or her job in your organisation. How do you face the bereaved family? What can you say?

2 Legal reasons

This is classed by some people as the CYA factor ('cover your ...').

Undoubtedly the law is being tightened up with more and more specific regulations. Indeed, all recently introduced regulations include a requirement to carry out risk assessments. However, this merely makes explicit what was implicit in the Health and Safety at Work Act 1974. In fact you could not fully comply with the Act without doing so.

An examination of the legal requirement for risk assessment under specific regulations is detailed in the next chapter.

3 Economic reasons

As mentioned in the introduction, there are enormous financial implications from the mismanagement of health and safety at work. Apart from the estimated cost to the UK economy of between £10 billion and £15 billion per year, the HSE have also estimated the hidden costs to organisations (see Figure 1 on page 7).

In any assessment of the possible losses incurred from accidents at work we should also take into account the following considerations:

- Loss of service to clients.

(continued on page 8)

Figure 1 The Accident Iceberg (source: HSE)

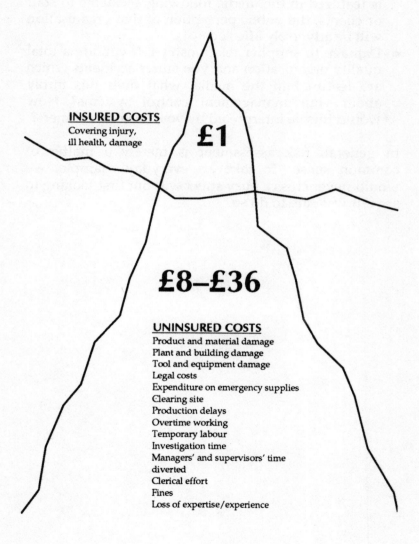

INSURED COSTS
Covering injury,
ill health, damage

£1

£8–£36

UNINSURED COSTS
Product and material damage
Plant and building damage
Tool and equipment damage
Legal costs
Expenditure on emergency supplies
Clearing site
Production delays
Overtime working
Temporary labour
Investigation time
Managers' and supervisors' time
diverted
Clerical effort
Fines
Loss of expertise/experience

- Damage to image. For example, when an organisation from the caring sector, such as a health service trust, is featured in the media following accidents to staff or clients, the public perception of that organisation will be adversely affected.
- Damage to supplier relationships. If you are a total quality organisation and you suffer accidents which are featured in the media, what does this imply about your management control systems? How would this be interpreted by your major customers?

In general, risk assessment is merely a matter of common sense. To take an everyday example, we would never cross a busy street without first looking to see if it was safe to do so.

2 Recent Legislation requiring Risk Assessment

To reiterate, all recent health and safety legislation makes explicit the implicit requirement to carry out risk assessments contained in the Health and Safety at Work Act 1974. You should always comply with the highest level of duty in any situation, which usually means the more specific regulations. Figure 2 shows how the levels of duty overlap, starting with the Health and Safety at Work Act 1974, moving through the Management of Health and Safety at Work Regulations 1992 and on to the most specific regulations.

This chapter aims to provide a **brief overview** of the most recent regulations.

Figure 2

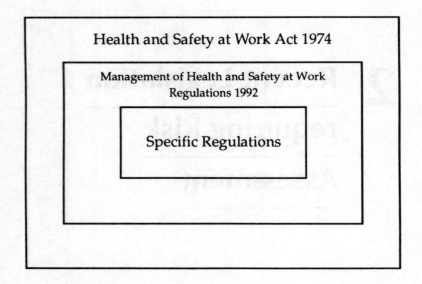

The Management of Health and Safety at Work Regulations 1992

The requirements of these regulations include the carrying out of a 'suitable and sufficient' assessment of all risks to the health and safety of employees and non-employees (in fact anyone) arising from work activities, together with the identification of the measures necessary to prevent injury.

A risk assessment that is suitable and sufficient for these regulations is defined in the ACOP (Approved Code Of Practice) as follows:

- It should identify the significant risks arising out of work.
- It should enable the employer or self-employed person to identify and prioritise the measures that need to be taken to comply with the relevant statutory provisions.
- It should be appropriate to the nature of the work and remain valid for a reasonable period of time.

The duty to assess risks under these regulations is a general duty to cover all eventualities arising at and from work. If a more specific regulation, *i.e.* COSHH (Control of Substances Hazardous to Health) or DSE (Display Screen Equipment), applies to an activity or situation, it will not be necessary to carry out another risk assessment to comply with this providing:

1 the assessment is still valid
2 the assessment is 'suitable and sufficient'.

Further requirements of these regulations are as follows:

- To make arrangements for implementing the health and safety measures identified by risk assessments. These cover planning, organisation, control, monitoring and reviews.
- To provide health surveillance where necessary.
- To appoint **competent** persons to assist in the implementation of the measures, necessary to comply with statutory requirements.
- To set up emergency procedures for serious and imminent danger, and danger areas.

- To provide employees with comprehensive and relevant information on health and safety matters.
- To co-operate with any other employer who shares a work site.
- To provide health and safety information for people working in their organisation who are not their employees (for example, the provision of risk assessments for contractors etc, and the obtaining of risk assessments from contractors).
- To appoint capable employees who can carry out their duties without risk to themselves or others, and to provide those employees with adequate training.
- Employees are duty-bound to use equipment in accordance with their training and statutory requirements. They are also obliged to inform the employer of any work situation they consider a serious and imminent danger and to report any shortcoming in the health and safety training and/or instructions they have received.
- Temporary workers and employment business workers must be provided with adequate health and safety information.
- The regulations also extend the current duties of employers to consult with safety representatives.

Remember, these regulations do not replace existing regulations such as the Health and Safety at Work Act 1974; they complement them. It should be noted that the language used in the regulations has become much stricter, replacing phrases such as 'in so far as is reasonably practicable' with the unambiguous 'employers shall ensure'.

What to do

The MOHSW regulations indicate that a systematic approach to health and safety management should be adopted. But, whilst the language of the regulations is strict, they do not specify the methods to be adopted when carrying out risk assessments. Therefore, organisations are free to develop systems to suit their individual needs (providing, of course, that they meet the requirements of the regulations).

Getting started

- Appoint a senior manager to be responsible for directing the health and safety programme.
- Check effectiveness of the safety committee. If necessary revitalise by training members.
- Purchase copies of the six HSE publications on the regulations.
- Review and update health and safety at work policy.
- Ensure that the organisation's communication systems for both briefing and consultation are effective.
- Carry out a programme of awareness training in the requirements of the regulations for all staff.
- Train managers in managing risk assessment.
- Select and train members of staff in risk assessment techniques.
- Commence a risk assessment programme on a rolling basis using a team-based approach, generating safe systems (preventive and protective measures) and involving employees in the process.
- Implement the measures as they are generated.
- Monitor the effectiveness of the measures.

- Set up a contractor management programme.
- Audit all procedures to check compliance, *e.g.* fire and evacuation procedures, training record system, etc.

The MOHSW regulations were amended as of 1 December 1994 to include:

Health and Safety Arrangements for New and Expectant Mothers

This affects women of child-bearing capacity in the workplace, where the work could, by reason of her condition, risk the health and safety of a new or expectant mother or her baby. It covers any processes or working conditions, physical or chemical agents, **including** those specified in Annexes I and II of Council Directive 92/85/EEC (detailed in Appendix 5).

The assessment required by regulation 3(1) of the MOHSW regulations 1992, shall also include such risk.

What to do

Clearly, this requires organisations who employ women of child-bearing capacity to extend their risk assessments to include risks that could affect new or expectant mothers.

Thus, systems should be established so that the employer is notified as soon as possible when an employee is pregnant or has recently given birth. The employer can then ensure (a) legal compliance and (b) prevent any harm to the woman and her unborn child or baby.

If it is established that a new or expectant mother is at risk she **must** be moved to suitable alternative work, or if no such work exists, be suspended on maternity grounds (full pay and benefits).

It is realistic strategy to audit all activities, processes, etc to identify anything that might constitute a risk to these women.

If such risks are present, as with any other type of risk, preventive and protective measures should be instituted.

Workplace (Health, Safety and Welfare) Regulations 1992

These regulations replace a number of existing pieces of legislation, including sections of the Factories Act 1961 and the Offices Shops and Railway Premises Act 1963. They cover most workplaces except means of transport, construction sites, mines, quarries and fishing boats. The regulations are phased. New or modified workplaces used for the first time after 31 December 1992 will have to comply immediately. Existing workplaces must comply by 1 January 1996.

The regulations are split into four broad areas:

1 **Working Environment**
   - including temperature, ventilation, room space, lighting, etc.

2 **Safety**
   - including safe passage of pedestrians and vehicles

15

- construction and safe opening, closing and cleaning of windows
- construction and condition of floors and doors, including slipping and tripping hazards, falls and falling objects.

3 Facilities
- including sanitary accommodation, clothing storage and rest areas.

Note: Rest facilities must include arrangements to protect non-smokers from tobacco smoke. Also rest facilities should be provided for pregnant women and nursing mothers.

4 Housekeeping
- including maintenance of the workplace, equipment and facilities, cleanliness and removal of waste materials.

What to do

- Carry out an audit of all the aspects covered in the regulations in all the organisation's workplaces.
- Apply risk assessment principles to the findings to establish priorities for action.
- Make managers and staff aware of the particular requirements of the regulations that affect them.
- When considering new premises or the modification of existing premises, ensure architects and similar specialists employed on the project are familiar with the regulations.

Provision and the Use of Work Equipment Regulations 1992

The HSE guidance to these regulations states that virtually all the requirements of PUWER already exist somewhere in law or constitute good practice. The regulations bring together these requirements and apply them across all industrial, commercial and service sectors.

This means that employers with well-chosen and well-maintained equipment should need to do little more than before.

The HSE view is that as many of the existing requirements are overlapped by PUWER, compliance with an existing requirement will normally be sufficient to comply with PUWER.

The regulations place a number of general duties on employers regarding:

- suitability of work equipment
- conditions in which it will be used
- maintenance in good order
- provision of adequate information, instruction and training to users (and their supervisors)
- provision of equipment that conforms with EC product directives.

There are a number of specific requirements covering:

- guarding
- protection against specific hazards

- work equipment parts and substances at high or very low temperatures
- control systems
- isolation from sources of energy
- maintenance operations
- warnings and markings.

Note: Work equipment is a very wide term covering such things as hand tools, computers, power presses, bottling plants, photocopiers and so on.

These regulations are also phased. **All equipment** must comply with regulations 1–10 covering suitability, maintenance, specific risks, information instruction and training, and conformity with EC product directives.

Any new, hired, leased or second-hand equipment brought into use in the workplace after 1 January 1993 must also immediately comply with remaining specific regulations 11–24 outlined above. Equipment in use before 1 January 1993 must comply with regulations 11–24 by 1 January 1997.

What to do

- Carry out an audit of all work equipment to assess level of compliance with the regulations.
- Apply risk assessment principles to establish priorities for action.
- Check adequacy of current training (and training records). These regulations have already been used in prosecutions for inadequate training!
- Carry out awareness training for all relevant staff.

- When contemplating purchasing, hiring, manufacturing (or in any way putting into first use) work equipment, ensure that it complies with these regulations, and in particular with the relevant EC product directive.

Some types of specific equipment such as display screen equipment have their own regulations (see p. 23). PUWER lays out general principles which should be followed where no such specific regulations are in existence.

Manual Handling Operations Regulations 1992

These regulations require employers to examine their manual handling operations in three key respects:

1 Hazardous manual handling operations should be avoided wherever possible. For example, could a load be moved by other means?
2 Any hazardous manual handling operation that cannot be avoided should be adequately assessed.
3 The risk of injury should be reduced as far as is reasonably practicable.

Employees have a duty to make full and proper use of any equipment or system provided for manual handling.

Manual handling means more than just lifting. It is defined as any transporting or supporting of a load (including lifting, putting down, pushing, pulling, carrying, moving by hand or bodily force).

These regulations result from research which showed that more than a quarter of all accidents reported each year involved manual handling.

What to do

One requirement of the regulations is for employers to inform their employees of the weights they are lifting and the heaviest side of any load whose centre of gravity is not distributed evenly. A practical way that organisations are addressing this is to get suppliers of components, consumable items etc, to mark the required information on the packaging.

- Carry out a risk assessment programme on all manual handling operations, taking into account the following factors:
  - the tasks
  - the loads
  - the working environment
  - individual capacity.
- Train key personnel as trainers in kinetic lifting techniques.
- Use these personnel to carry out a training programme for all staff involved in manual handling.
- Appoint trained staff in each department as manual handling assessors to advise other staff on unusual lifts etc.
- Communicate with all staff the requirements of these regulations via briefing and consultation.

The success of compliance with these regulations depends greatly on having an educated and aware workforce.

There is an excellent checklist for carrying out manual handling risk assessments in the HSE publication *Guidance to Manual Handling Regulations*.

Personal Protective Equipment at Work Regulations 1992

These regulations cover:

- Risk assessment and selection of suitable personal protective equipment (PPE). This risk assessment is designed to cover those risks which have not been prevented by other means.
- Review of the risk assessment when you suspect that it is no longer valid or when significant changes have affected the matters to which it relates.
- Provision of suitable PPE.
- Compatibility of PPE. If more than one item of PPE has to be worn then they should be compatible and continue to provide effective protection against risk.
- PPE should be effectively maintained.
- Appropriate accommodation should be provided for PPE when it is not in use.
- Adequate information, instruction and training should be provided.
- It is the duty of employers to take all reasonable steps to ensure that PPE is properly used, and the duty of employees to use any PPE provided in accordance with instructions and training.

21

- Employees who have been provided with PPE shall report any loss or obvious defect immediately.

PPE is defined as all equipment (including weather-proof clothing) which is intended to be worn or held by a person at work and which protects his/her health and safety. This excludes such things as ordinary clothing, PPE for road transport, sports equipment, etc.

Suitable PPE:

- is appropriate for the risk(s) involved and the conditions where the exposure to risk(s) may occur
- takes account of ergonomic requirements and the health of the user
- fits the wearer correctly, with appropriate adjustment for the range of its design
- so far as is practicable, is effective in preventing or adequately controlling the risk(s) involved without itself introducing additional risk
- complies with legislation governing its design, manufacture and use.

Employers have duties to assess risks and not to rely on PPE if other measures can be taken.

What to do

- Carry out risk assessments.
- Ensure that PPE is only used as a last resort (beware of treating the symptoms of a situation by using PPE when you should be dealing with the root cause).
- Consult with workers when selecting PPE.

- Instruct and train in correct use of PPE.
- Provide appropriate accommodation for PPE.
- Set up systems of inspection and maintenance of PPE.
- Ensure that it is used properly.

Note: This last point may be troublesome for organisations that allow discipline to become slack in this area, *e.g.* tolerating employees who do not wear eye protection in designated eye protection areas, or safety shoes when there is a risk of foot injuries.

- Check and update disciplinary procedures, consult with employees and brief them about the reasons for the stricter regulations.
- Train managers, supervisors and first line leaders in handling discipline in a positive way.

Health and Safety (Display Screen Equipment) Regulations 1992

The requirements of these regulations include:

- analysis of workstations and identification of measures to reduce risks (risk assessment)
- requirements for workstations
- daily routine of users
- protection of eyes and eyesight
- provision of information and training.

Workstations in use before 31 January 1992 will have until 31 December 1996 to comply with the minimum requirements for workstations (regulation 3 and schedule). Any workstation first put into use after 1 January 1993 will have to comply immediately. However, as employers frequently reorganise workstations, it would be advisable to forget the phasing and ensure that you comply.

What to do

- Carry out risk assessment, analysing the workstations and the daily routines of users.
- Train the users to do their own risk assessments, possibly by using a checklist approach, and train them in safe working practices.
- Train managers and supervisory staff in supervising risk assessments.
- Ensure that the work routine of users is properly planned, so that frequent changes of activity take place.
- Provide appropriate eyesight testing at users' request.
- Ensure that equipment conforms to EC standards.

You are strongly advised to obtain from the HSE their 6 booklets on these regulations. They contain not only the regulations but also approved codes of practice and guidance on how to comply with the regulations.

3 Recent Legislation requiring Risk Assessment (Northern Ireland)

Health and safety legislation in Northern Ireland mirrors the legislation in Great Britain, but there are some differences in detail. This chapter outlines those differences where they affect the requirement for risk assessments to be carried out.

The health and safety advisory and enforcement system in Northern Ireland

Health and safety advisory and enforcement activities in Northern Ireland are not carried out by the Health and Safety Commission (HSC) and Health and Safety Executive (HSE) of Great Britain. Northern Ireland has its own organisations fulfilling these functions:

1 The Health and Safety Agency (HSA)

This public body was set up under the Health and Safety at Work (Northern Ireland) Order 1978.

The HSA has a similar role to the HSC in Great Britain, but has fewer direct links with the separate enforcing authority.

The HSA seeks to secure and promote the health, safety and welfare of people at work and protect all other people against risks to their health and safety from work-related activities.

It provides an extensive information and advisory service (including details of legislation, approved codes of practice, guidance notes, videos, etc), appraises all proposed regulations and monitors existing regulations.

2 The Department of Economic Development, Health and Safety Division, Health and Safety Inspectorate (HSI)

This is the prime enforcement body, and was also set up under the Health and Safety at Work (Northern Ireland) Order 1978.

The HSI is responsible for enforcement in workplaces such as factories, building sites, mines and quarries. Enforcement in other workplaces in Northern Ireland is the responsibility of different bodies:

- farms – the Department of Agriculture
- offices, shops, restaurants and similar workplaces – the District Council for the area.

The powers of enforcement officers under the Health and Safety at Work (Northern Ireland) Order 1978, mirror those of enforcement officers in Great Britain.

All recent Northern Ireland health and safety legislation includes an explicit duty to carry out risk assessments. The Health and Safety at Work (Northern Ireland) Order 1978, which mirrors the Health and Safety at Work Act 1974, carries only an implicit requirement to assess risks. You should always comply with the highest level of duty in any situation, which usually means the more specific regulations.

Here is an example of how this works in practice:

- The **Manual Handling Operations Regulations (Northern Ireland) 1992** place a specific requirement on employers to make a 'suitable and sufficient' risk assessment of all such manual handling operations.
- The **Management of Health and Safety at Work Regulations (Northern Ireland) 1992** place a general requirement on employers to make a 'suitable and sufficient' assessment of the health and safety risks their employees face at work.
- The **Health and Safety at Work (Northern Ireland) Order 1978** includes the duty of employers to provide arrangements for ensuring, so far as is reasonably practicable, safety and absence of risks to health in connection with the use, handling, storage and transport of articles and substances.

- A risk assessment properly carried out under the specific requirements of the Manual Handling Operations Regulations would satisfy the more general requirements of the other two pieces of legislation. However, where no such specific regulations exist, these pieces of legislation still require risk assessments to be carried out.

Figure 3 shows how the levels of duty overlap, starting with the Health and Safety at Work (Northern Ireland) Order 1978, moving through the Management of Health and Safety at Work Regulations (Northern Ireland) 1992 and on to the most specific regulations.

Figure 3

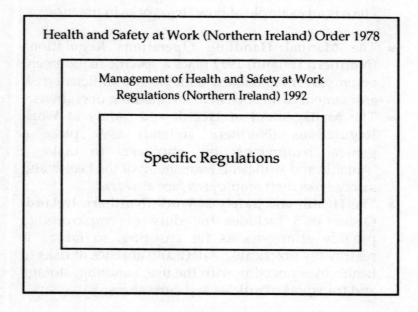

Health and Safety at Work (Northern Ireland) Order 1978

Management of Health and Safety at Work
Regulations (Northern Ireland) 1992

Specific Regulations

The rest of this chapter provides a brief overview of recent regulations regarding risk assessment. The main details are identical to the equivalent regulations outlined in Chapter 2. Detail differences are indicated.

Management of Health and Safety at Work Regulations (Northern Ireland) 1992
● Details as those in Chapter 2.

Workplace (Health, Safety and Welfare) Regulations (Northern Ireland) 1993
● Details mostly the same as those in Chapter 2, but with different implementation dates.
● The regulations came into force on 8 March 1993.
● Regulations 5–27 and schedules come into force on 1 January 1996.
● New workplace means a workplace used for the first time as a workplace after 7 March 1993.

Provision and Use of Work Equipment Regulations (Northern Ireland) 1993
● Details mostly the same as those in Chapter 2, but with different implementation dates.
● The regulations came into force on 22 February 1993.
● These regulations are phased. All equipment must comply with regulations 1–10 covering suitability, maintenance, specific risks, information, instruction and training, and conformity with EC product directives.
● Any new, hired, leased or second-hand equipment brought into use in the workplace after 22 February 1993 must also immediately comply with remaining regulations 11–24. These include guarding, specified

hazards, high/low temperatures, controls, isolation, stability, lighting, design for maintenance and markings/warnings.
- Equipment in use before 22 February 1993 must comply with regulations 11–24 by 1 January 1997.

Manual Handling Operations Regulations (Northern Ireland) 1992
- Details as those in Chapter 2, but with different implementation dates.
- These regulations came into force on 8 January 1993.

Personal Protective Equipment at Work Regulations (Northern Ireland) 1993
- Details as those in Chapter 2, but with different implementation dates.
- These regulations came into force on 22 February 1993.

Health and Safety (Display Screen Equipment) Regulations (Northern Ireland) 1992
- Details as those in Chapter 2.

You are strongly advised to obtain from the HSA their 6 booklets on these regulations. They contain not only the regulations but also approved codes of practice and guidance on how to comply with the regulations.

4 Methods of Carrying Out Risk Assessments

The various regulations do not define how risk assessments should be carried out. They are only a guide as to what the outcome of risk assessment should be. This allows us, therefore, to select a method that suits our organisation's particular needs.

In this chapter we outline some popular and effective methods that are currently in use.

Important definitions

Hazard – something with the potential to cause harm.
Risk – the likelihood of that potential to do harm being realised.
Risk assessment – a process of identifying the hazards in any work situation and making a competent judgement

as to the likelihood of that hazard actually causing a risk of harm. Rating the severity of that risk and identifying measures to ensure that the risks are eliminated or, if that is not possible, adequately controlled so as to prevent harm.

Preventive and protective measures – measures that have to be taken as a result of carrying out a risk assessment. Some are dependant on the specific legislation, but HSE guidance is as follows:

- If possible avoid the risk altogether.
- Combat risks at source.
- Wherever possible adapt the work to the individual.
- Take advantage of technological and technical progress.
- Ensure that risk prevention measures form part of a coherent policy and approach.
- Give priority to those measures which protect the whole workplace and those who work there or visit.
- Ensure that workers understand what is expected of them.
- The measures should be part of an approach that builds an active health and safety culture into the organisation.

Suitable and sufficient risk assessment – this is required by the regulations and should:

- identify the significant risks arising out of work activity
- identify and prioritise the measures needed to comply with the relevant statutory provisions

- be appropriate to the nature of the work being carried out and remain valid for a reasonable period of time.

The combating of risk at source is an important point to grasp. All too often we treat the symptom rather than the root cause. If we regularly find water on the floor, it is important we clean it up to prevent people slipping on it. But it is vital that we repair the faulty tap which is the real cause of the risk.

Examples of risk assessment methods

The following are examples of methods currently being used by organisations.

5 steps to risk assessment

This easy-to-use system is published by the HSE in Great Britain and the HSA in Northern Ireland.
   This well thought out two-piece form consists of one sheet giving useful advice to guide the user through each of the 5 steps. The second sheet has headings and prompts for the steps, with a column under each heading to record your findings.
   The 5 steps to risk assessment are:

1 Look for hazards.
2 Decide who might be harmed, and how.
3 Evaluate the risks arising from the hazards and decide whether existing precautions are adequate or require further action.

4 Record your findings.
5 Review your assessment from time to time and revise it if necessary.

This system should be suitable for most organisations, although some have commented that it is not sophisticated enough. However, it is our experience that simple effective systems get used, and, more importantly, deliver the required result!

See Appendix 3 for the HSE risk assessment form.

Team-based risk assessment

This is another easy-to-use form-based system that ensures the risk assessment process is a team activity.

Developed by The Industrial Society, this system is based on the logic that drives such initiatives as quality circles and product improvement groups. It harnesses people's creative powers and involves them not just with designing safer working practices but with more productive and economic outcomes.

The process of team-based risk assessment

- The motivating principle is to get the people closest to the action involved, as in product improvement groups.
- The team studies workplace method(s) by breaking down the activity into its component parts (easily digestible chunks) and asking the following questions about each stage:

1 Are any hazards present?
2 Do those hazards represent a risk? If so, do we rate the risk as low, medium or high?
3 Are we using the most appropriate method, equipment or material for what we are trying to achieve?
4 If we are, what controlling actions are necessary?
5 How are the controls to be implemented?
6 When?
7 Who is involved?
8 What monitoring should be carried out, how often and by whom?

● The team should then be encouraged to estimate:
  a the cost of any changes required
  b the likely benefits of proposed changes.

You can illustrate how this works in practice by using the example of the sharpening of a pencil with a penknife.

The trainees assess this task as a team-based risk assessment, breaking it down into key stages. It is quickly ascertained that the wrong method is being used for the job, and that a pencil sharpener would be better.

Making that simple change helps avoid potentially expensive and painful accidents, saves on raw materials (pencils – and possibly fingers!), makes the job faster, and requires less skill and attention. The quality of the output is also improved.

This is a very simple example of an unsafe, incorrect method. But just consider how many examples of this type are present in our workplaces?

Figure 3 shows a typical team-based risk assessment form.

Figure 3

TEAM-BASED RISK ASSESSMENT FORM						
Carried out by... Date...........................						
Description of activity/situation/process						
Key stages	Hazards present	Risks	L	M	H	Controlling action
Action required						
Date required			Date monitored			
Cost/Benefit estimates			Monitored by			

An **Assessment Checklist Proforma** (Appendix 2) such as the one provided in Training Direct's video-based training package, *A Complete Guide to Risk Assessment*, is another method in current use. (Further details of this video pack may be obtained direct from Training Direct – see Appendix 1.)

Computer-based risk assessment systems

There are numerous examples of computer-based risk assessment systems available, so it's important to consider the following points before selecting this option:

- Will it fulfil the organisation's needs? Is it flexible enough to be used to carry out a risk assessment programme without having to utilise more traditional methods as well?
- How difficult is it to operate, bearing in mind that we wish to involve those closest to the action? How long will it take to train them in its use?

One package the we have used and found to be effective is GEE Publishing's *Health and Safety Lawbase*, which features useful legal awareness modules as well as an easy-to-use risk assessment facility (see References for details).

Risk rating

A factor common to all systems is the need for some means of rating the risks assessed so as to allocate priorities for action and estimate cost.

A number of systems feature the simple concept of applying **low**, **medium** or **high** to the assessed risk, with the 'highs' taking priority.

This will be perfectly adequate for a great many organisations which operate in low-risk environments. Other organisations, however, due to the nature of their processes etc, have a number of inherent risks of varying severity which need to be classified and managed accordingly. It is also the case that many managers are more comfortable with **numerical rating systems**. These are many and varied but share certain characteristics:

- Applying numbers to indicate the severity of hazard potential and the likelihood of the realisation of risk.
- Rating those numerical factors in a given circumstance.
- Multiplying these factors together to give a rating.

A point to bear in mind when designing or choosing such a system is not to have a large scale of gradation for hazard and risk. I have seen systems that range from 0–200 for each! This will only confuse those who use the system and will lead to inconsistent results. Bear in mind also that some people have an aversion to numbers which could get in the way of successful risk assessment.

Remember, simple systems work. Figure 4 shows a simple numerical system.

Figure 4 Assessing the relative importance of health and safety risks (source: HSE)

Simple risk estimation

Hazards   The potential to cause harm will vary in severity. The effect of a hazard may, for example, be rated:

3. **Major** – *e.g.* death or major injury

2. **Serious** – *e.g.* injuries where people may be off work for more than 3 days

1. **Slight** – *e.g.* all other injuries, including those where people are off work for periods of up to 3 days

Risks   The likelihood of that potential to do harm being realised. Likelihood of harm may be rated:

3. **High** – where it is certain or near certain that harm will occur

2. **Medium** – where harm will frequently occur

1. **Low** – where harm will seldom occur

Risk = Hazard x Likelihood of x Number of persons
        severity   occurrence   exposed to the risk

Taking into account the definitions and requirements of the various regulations and looking at current best practice, we have designed a risk assessment-based health and safety management process which can be used as a guiding set of general principles in carrying out the risk assessments.

This should be suitable for most organisations and complies with legislation. More importantly, it is practical and easy to use.

It must be stressed again, however, that no one model is suitable for all types of organisations. Whatever system you choose, it will need 'customising' to suit the needs of the organisation.

A risk assessment-based health and safety management process

1 Look at what is actually happening in the workplace
This means walking the job, observing, talking and listening to people. For instance, what is the normal work activity? Does it follow the guidelines outlined in the operating manual or has there been some 'drift'? What happens in pressure/abnormal situations?

2 Look for any hazards
Those closest to the 'action' are in the best situation to know what really goes on, so involve them in the assessment. Rate the severity of the hazard. Record the findings.

3 Do these hazards represent any risk?

Are the hazards adequately controlled, or should more be done to prevent the realisation of the 'potential to cause harm'? What is the severity of the risk? How many people could be affected? Again, it is vital that those who work in the area, or use the equipment/ methods, are fully involved. Record the findings.

4 Design safe systems of work

Design protective and preventive measures to eliminate or adequately control any risks. Using the team approach to do this is vital. People will support what they have had a hand in creating. People are ingenious, and this provides an excellent opportunity to tap the talent that undoubtedly exists. The result is often not only safer working practices but also improvements in service, efficiency and effectiveness.

5 Implement the safe system of work

This is a vital stage, and one which is often handled poorly. Implementation will need education, communication, commitment and enthusiasm or it will not be effective. Avoid the 'fine words in filing cabinets' syndrome at all costs.

6 Monitoring

Is it happening? As in 1 above, walk the job, talk and listen to people. Look for evidence that the safe systems are being used.

7 Evaluation

Is the safe system of work achieving the objective it was designed for? Is there any residual risk? Take measurements of health and safety performance. Have any factors changed since the original risk assessment? If so, the risk assessment process should be repeated.

5 How to Set Up a Risk Assessment Programme

Many people find it difficult to know just how to start a risk assessment programme. So, after talking to several different types of organisation, we have come up with the following suggestions:

- Appoint a senior manager to be responsible for the introduction of the risk assessment programme. Allocate it as a personal target for that manager, whose performance should be measured in this area as it would for other business activities.
- Discuss and agree upon a risk assessment policy. It should involve every member of staff. Define the methods to be used, select a paperwork system, etc. Everyone should be briefed as to their

responsibilities. This could well be a case for team briefing.

- It could be useful to adopt a 'model' system, customised to suit the organisation. But ensure that the model is adapted to suit the practices of the organisation, and not vice versa.
- Ensure that managers receive appropriate training in health and safety responsibilities and risk assessment techniques.
- Assess managers on their health and safety performance.
- Ensure that all those who are taking part in carrying out risk assessments receive appropriate training.
- Agree upon and publish a programme for carrying out risk assessments in the organisation, with dates, targets and allocation of responsibilities.
- Monitor the progress of the risk assessment programme via a safety committee as well as the managerial monitoring system.

The decisions on priorities for risk assessment may well emerge from a process such as 'rough risk assessment'. This process typically consists of the following steps:

1 Gather available evidence from accident statistics and reports, 'near miss' reports, and talking to staff about what they regard as problem areas.
2 Compile a 'what's happening list' for each department or section. Get a competent person from each department to help.
3 Use some form of simple recording system that will give you an instant picture of what the health and safety issues are.

What to look at:

- people
- equipment
- workplace (environment)
- materials
- procedures/operations.

What to record:

- significant findings
- existing control measures
- population affected.

Having done this you can start the detailed risk assessment process by concentrating on those risks that are prominent in the organisation.

The key to success at this early stage is to actively involve people at every opportunity, and to make your commitment to the risk assessment process clear. This will help counter the negative effect of cynics who will, if given the chance, label this yet another 'management flavour of the month'.

6 Assessing Effectiveness

The effectiveness of your risk assessment programme can be judged by monitoring the following incidences:

- A reduction in the accident rate.
- A reduction in the losses due to health and safety incidents.
- A reduction in the absentee rate.
- An increase in output and/or service provided.

In considering the measurement of performance, the HSE publication *Successful Health and Safety Management* refers to:

- **active** systems which monitor the achievement of plans and the extent of compliance with standards; and

- **reactive** systems which monitor accidents, ill health and incidents.

The latter is obviously important and should be carried out thoroughly using effect systems. The former is of more interest when it comes to getting things done.

Risk assessment programmes should be part of the performance management system of the organisation. Managers need to agree targets for the implementation of the risk assessment programme, and performance against these targets should be a feature of review interviews throughout the management structure.

As a guiding principle for risk assessment, it is worth bearing in mind the old adage, 'what gets measured gets done'.

7 References

Reference Publications

The Costs of Accidents at Work
HSE HS(G) 96
ISBN 0 11 886374 6
By HSE

Successful Health and Safety Management
HSE HS(G) 65
ISBN 0 11 885988 9
By HSE

Management of Health and Safety at Work
Approved Code of Practice
ISBN 0 11 886330 4
By HSC

Workplace Health, Safety and Welfare
Approved Code of Practice and Guidance L24
ISBN 0 11 886333 9
By HSC

Work Equipment
Guidance on Regulations L22
ISBN 0 11 886332 0
By HSE

Personal Protective Equipment at Work
Guidance on Regulations L25
ISBN 0 11 886334 7
By HSE

Manual Handling
Guidance on Regulations L23
ISBN 0 11 886335 5
By HSE

Display Screen Equipment Work
Guidance on Regulations L26
ISBN 0 11 886331 2
By HSE

The Legal Framework of Health and Safety at Work in Northern Ireland
Booklet 73 HSA 95
By HSA for Northern Ireland

Management of Health and Safety at Work in Northern Ireland
Approved Code of Practice HSA 61
ISBN 0 337 11184 7
By HSA for Northern Ireland

Workplace Health, Safety and Welfare (Northern Ireland)
Approved Code of Practice and Guidance HSA 66
ISBN 0 337 11191 X
By HSA for Northern Ireland

Work Equipment, Provision and Use of Work Equipment Regulations (Northern Ireland) 1993
Guidance on Regulations HSA 65
ISBN 0 337 11190 1
By HSA for Northern Ireland

Manual Handling (Northern Ireland)
Guidance on Regulations HSA 68
ISBN 0 337 11193 6
By HSA for Northern Ireland

Personal Protective Equipment at Work (Northern Ireland)
Guidance on Regulations HSA 69
ISBN 0 337 11194 4
By HSA for Northern Ireland

Display Screen Equipment Work (Northern Ireland)
Guidance on Regulations HSA 67
ISBN 0 337 11192 8
By HSA for Northern Ireland

Health and Safety Lawbase – a computer-based
reference and risk assessment tool
By GEE Publishing Limited
South Quay Plaza
183 Marsh Wall
London E14 9FS
Tel: 0171 538 5386

A Complete Guide to Risk Assessment – a video-based
training package
By Training Direct
Longman House
Burnt Mill
Harlow
Essex CM20 2JE
Tel: 01279 623850

8   **Appendices**

Appendix 1

Useful Addresses

HSE Information Centre
Broad Lane
Sheffield S3 7HQ
Tel: 0114 2892345

HSE Books
PO Box 1999
Sudbury
Suffolk CO10 6FS
Tel: 01787 881165

HSA (Northern Ireland)
Canada House
22 North Street
Belfast BT 1NW
Tel: 01232 243249

Training Direct
Longman House
Burnt Mill
Harlow
Essex CM20 2JE
Tel: 01279 623850
(publishers of the video package *A Complete Guide to Risk Assessment*)

Appendix 2

Assessment Checklist Proforma

1. General	
Assessment no:	
Assessed by:	
Date of assessment:	
Person assessed:	
Department:	
Works no:	
Task assessed:	
2. Hazards	
Are there any hazards likely to affect health and safety?	1: 2: 3: 4: 5: 6:
3. Risks	
Is the likelihood of the hazard(s) causing actual harm: low, medium or high?	1: 2: 3: 4: 5: 6:

4. Risk Assessment	
Is the likelihood of the hazard and the risk coming together: low, medium or high?	1: 2: 3: 4: 5: 6:
Can the hazard(s) be removed? Yes? No?	1: 2: 3: 4: 5: 6:
Can the risk(s) be removed? Yes? No?	1: 2: 3: 4: 5: 6:
5. Control	
Can the hazard(s) be controlled by: A change in process, equipment or environment?	1: 2: 3: 4: 5: 6:

Can the hazard(s) be controlled by: A change in working methods?	1: 2: 3: 4: 5: 6:
Can the risks(s) be controlled by: Personal protective equipment?	1: 2: 3: 4: 5: 6:
Can the risks(s) be controlled by: Information, training or instruction?	1: 2: 3: 4: 5: 6:
6. Physical Characteristics	
Does the person have any physical complaint/problem likely to affect his/her ability to work safely or in good health? Yes? No?	

7. Emergency Procedures	
Are there clear emergency procedures? Yes? No?	
Is the person aware of these procedures? Yes? No?	
8. Action	
What immediate action should be taken?	1: 2: 3: 4: 5: 6:
What subsequent action should be taken?	1: 2: 3: 4: 5: 6:

What monitoring procedures (if any) should be put in place?	1: 2: 3: 4: 5: 6:
9. Review	
When should this assessment be reviewed?	
Assessment completed?	
Signed:	
Date filed:	

Reproduced by kind permission of Training Direct

ASSESSMENT OF RISK FOR

Company Name

Company Address

HAZARD

Look only for hazards which you could reasonably expect to result in significant harm under the conditions in your workplace. Use the following examples as a guide:-

- Slipping/tripping hazards (eg poorly maintained floors or stairs)
- Fire (eg from flammable materials)
- Chemicals (eg Battery Acid)
- Moving parts of machinery (eg blades)
- Work at height (eg from mezzanine floors)
- Ejection of material (eg from plastic moulding)
- Pressure systems (eg steam boilers)
- Vehicles (eg fork-lift trucks)
- Electricity (eg poor wiring)
- Dust (eg from grinding)
- Fume (eg welding)
- Manual handling
- Noise
- Poor lighting
- Low temperature

List hazards here:

WHO MIGHT BE HARMED?

There is no need to list individuals by name — just think about groups of people doing similar work or who may be affected, eg:-

- Office staff
- Maintenance personnel
- Contractors
- People sharing your workplace
- Operators
- Cleaners
- Members of the public

Pay particular attention to:-

- Staff with disabilities
- Visitors
- Inexperienced staff
- Lone workers

They may be more vulnerable.

List groups of people who are especially at risk from the significant hazards which you have identified:

60

Post code

IS THE RISK ADEQUATELY CONTROLLED?

Have you already taken precautions against the risks from the hazards you listed? For example, have you provided:-

- Adequate information, instruction or training?
- Adequate systems or procedures?

Do the precautions:-

- Meet the standards set by a legal requirement?
- Comply with a recognised industry standard?
- Represent good practice?
- Reduce risk as far as reasonably practicable?

If so, then the risks are adequately controlled, but you need to indicate the precautions you have in place. You may refer to procedures, manuals, company rules, etc giving this information.

List existing controls here or note where the information may be found:

WHAT FURTHER ACTION IS NECESSARY TO CONTROL THE RISK?

What more could you reasonably do for those risks which you found were not adequately controlled?

You will need to give priority to those risks which affect large numbers of people and/or could result in serious harm. Apply the principles below when taking further action, if possible in the following order:-

- Remove the risk completely
- Try a less risky option
- Prevent access to the hazard (eg by guarding)
- Organise work to reduce exposure to the hazard
- Issue personal protective equipment
- Provide welfare facilities (eg washing facilities for removal of contamination and first-aid)

List the risks which are not adequately controlled and the action you will take where it is reasonably practicable to do more. You are entitled to take cost into account, unless the risk is high:

61

List hazards here:

List groups of people who are especially at risk from the significant hazards which you have identified:

List existing controls here or note where the information may be found:	**List the risks which are not adequately controlled and the action you will take where it is reasonably practicable to do more. You are entitled to take cost into account, unless the risk is high:**

Appendix 4

How The Industrial Society can Help

The Industrial Society can help you to become more successful in health and safety management. We have a nationwide team of qualified health and safety specialists who also have an in-depth knowledge of managerial skills.

Our approach is typically based on a four stage process:

1 **Investigation** – we work with you to analyse accurately your needs, discuss possible answers to them and set objectives in the form of measurable outcomes.
2 **Design** – we draw together the components of a development package to meet your specific needs and address the objectives.
3 **Delivery** – we deliver the package, whether in the form of training or consultancy, using the most gifted and knowledgeable presenters.
4 **Evaluation/support** – we assess the effectiveness of the work we have carried out against pre-determined objectives, and provide ongoing support to help the organisation develop its own answers.

Appendix 5

Non-exhaustive list of Agents, Processes and Working Conditions

Referred to in Article 4(1) of EC Directive on Pregnant Workers

A. Agents
1. *Physical agents* where these are regarded as agents causing foetal lesions and/or likely to disrupt placental attachment, and in particular:
   (a) shocks, vibration or movement;
   (b) handling of loads entailing risks, particularly of a dorsolumbar nature;
   (c) noise;
   (d) ionizing radiation;
   (e) non-ionizing radiation;
   (f) extremes of cold or heat;
   (g) movements and postures, travelling – either inside or outside the establishment – mental and physical fatigue and other physical burdens connected with the activity of the worker within the meaning of Article 2 of the Directive.
2. *Biological agents*
   Biological agents of risk groups 2, 3 and 3 within the meaning of Article 2(d) numbers, 2, 3 and 4 of Directive 90/679/EEC, in so far as it is known that these agents or the therapeutic measures necessitated by such agents endanger the health of pregnant women and the unborn child and in so far as they do not yet appear in Annex II.
3. *Chemical agents*
   The following chemical agents in so far as it is known that they endanger the health of pregnant women and the unborn child an in so far as they do not yet appear in Annex II:
   (a) substances labelled R 40, R 45, R 46, and R 47 under Directive 67/548/EEC in so far as they do not yet appear in Annex II;
   (b) chemical agents in Annex I to Directive 90/394/EEC;

(c) mercury and mercury derivatives;
(d) antimitotic drugs;
(e) carbon monoxide;
(f) chemical agents of known and dangerous percutaneous absorption.

B. Process
Industrial processes listed in Annex I to Directive 90/394/EEC.

C. Working conditions
Underground mining work.

Referred to in Article 6 of EC Directive on Pregnant Workers

A. Pregnant workers within the meaning of Article 2(a)
1. *Agents*
   (a) Physical agents
   Work in hyperbaric atmosphere, *e.g.* pressurized enclosures and underwater diving.
   (b) Biological agents
   The following biological agents:
   – toxoplasma,
   – rubella virus,
   unless the pregnant workers are proved to be adequately protected against such agents by immunization.
   (c) Chemical agents
   Lead and lead derivatives in so far as these agents are capable of being absorbed by the human organism.
2. *Working conditions*
   Underground mining work.

D. Workers who are breastfeeding within the meaning of Article 2(c)
1. *Agents*
   (a) Chemical agents
   Lead and lead derivatives in so far as these agents are capable of being absorbed by the human organism.
2. *Working conditions*
   Underground mining work.